<吹奏楽譜（小編成） Small Band>

SBL-20-005

FULL SCORE

Grade 2.5

小編成

楽器紹介のための ミッキーマウス・マーチ

Mickey Mouse March ～Introduction of wind instruments～

作曲：Jimmie Dodd
編曲：郷間幹男

楽器編成表

Flute	B♭ Trumpet 1	Drums
(Piccolo)	B♭ Trumpet 2	Timpani
Oboe	F Horn 1	Percussion 1
B♭ Clarinets 1 & 2	F Horn 2	...Crash Cymbals,Tambourine,
B♭ Clarinet 3	Trombone 1	Vibraphone
Bass Clarinet	Trombone 2	Percussion 2
Alto Saxophones 1 (& *2*)	Euphonium	...Bass Drum, Sus.Cymbal,
Tenor Saxophone	Tuba	Ratchet,Wind Chime,
Baritone Saxophone	Electric Bass	Sleigh Bell,Flexatone,
	(String Bass) ※パート譜のみ	Glokenspiel
		Piano Score
		・Melody (in C)
		・*Piano*
		Full Score

＊イタリック表記の楽譜はオプション

楽器紹介のための
ミッキーマウス・マーチ
Mickey Mouse March ~Introduction of wind instruments~

Jimmie Dodd 作曲
郷間幹男 編曲

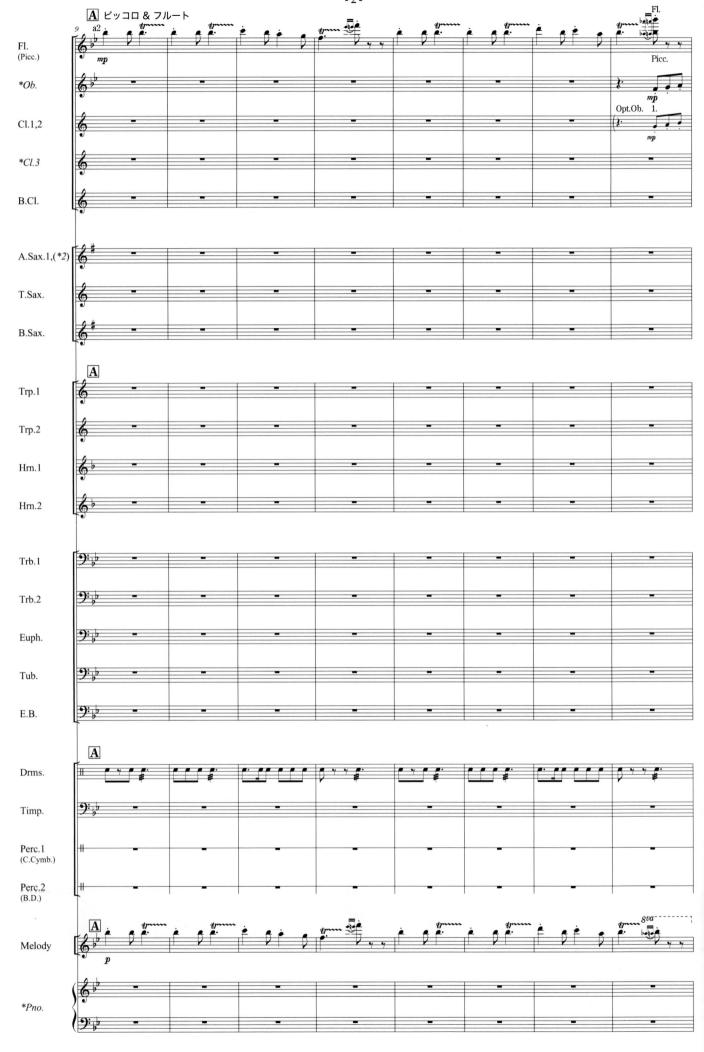

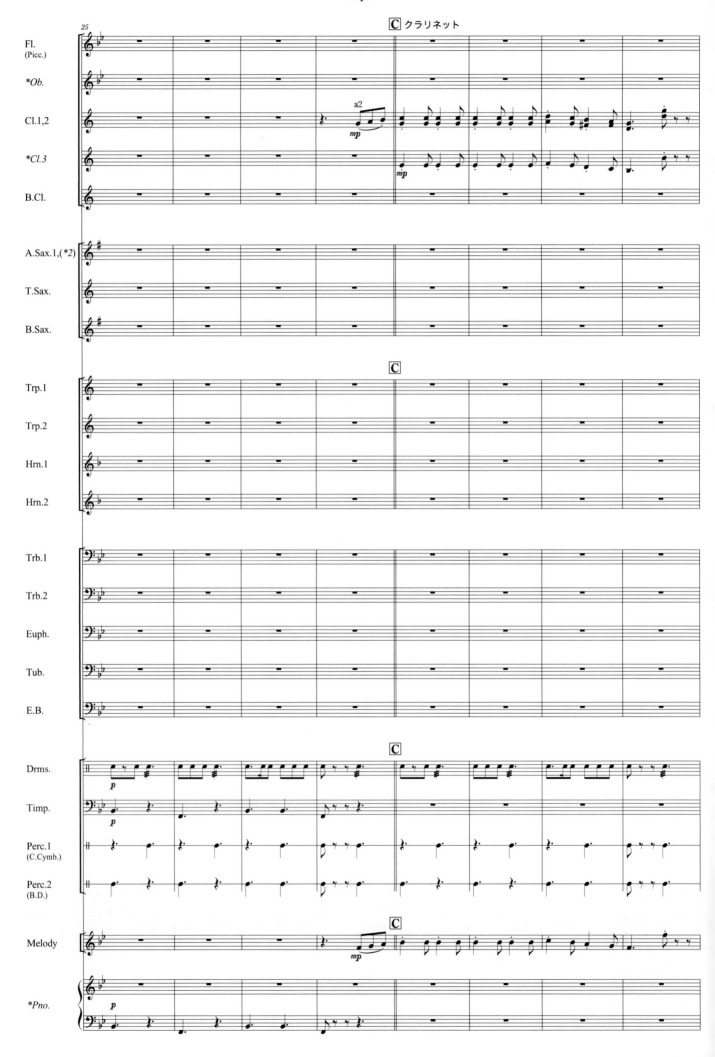

ご注文について

楽譜のご注文はウィンズスコアのWEBサイト、または、全国の楽器店ならびに書店にて。

◎当社WEBサイトでのご注文

winds-score.com

右側のQRコードよりWEBサイトへアクセスし、ご注文ください。

◎ご注文方法に関しての詳細は、右側のQRコードより
　ご確認いただけます。

TEL:0120-713-771　　FAX:03-6809-0594

※この出版物の全部または一部を権利者に無断で複製（コピー）することは、著作権の侵害にあたり、著作権法により罰せられます。

※造本には十分注意しておりますが、万一、落丁・乱丁などの不良品がありましたらお取り替えいたします。
また、ご意見・ご感想もホームページより受け付けておりますので、お気軽にお問い合わせください。

Oboe

楽器紹介のための
ミッキーマウス・マーチ
Mickey Mouse March ~Introduction of wind instruments~

Jimmie Dodd 作曲
郷間幹男 編曲

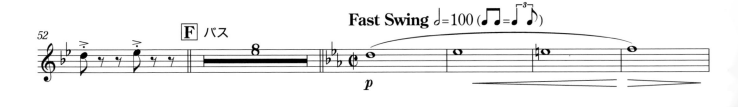

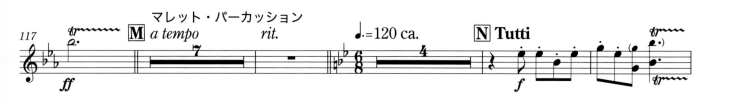

B♭ Clarinet 3

楽器紹介のための
ミッキーマウス・マーチ
Mickey Mouse March ~Introduction of wind instruments~

Jimmie Dodd 作曲
郷間幹男 編曲

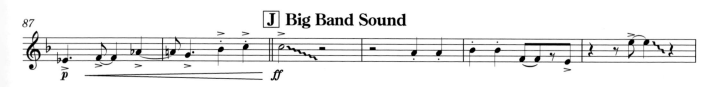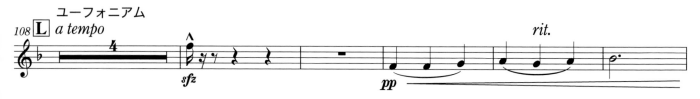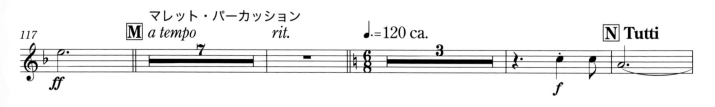

ミッキーマウス・マーチ

Bass Clarinet

楽器紹介のための
Mickey Mouse March ~Introduction of wind instruments~

Jimmie Dodd 作曲
郷間幹男 編曲

Alto Saxophones 1&2

楽器紹介のための
ミッキーマウス・マーチ
Mickey Mouse March ~Introduction of wind instruments~

Jimmie Dodd 作曲
郷間幹男 編曲

Tenor Saxophone

楽器紹介のための
ミッキーマウス・マーチ
Mickey Mouse March ~Introduction of wind instruments~

Jimmie Dodd 作曲
郷間幹男 編曲

MEMO

Electric Bass

楽器紹介のための
ミッキーマウス・マーチ
Mickey Mouse March ~Introduction of wind instruments~

Jimmie Dodd 作曲
郷間幹男 編曲

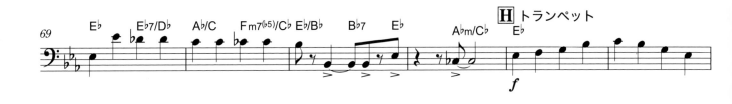

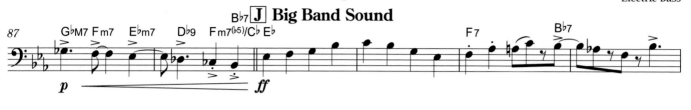

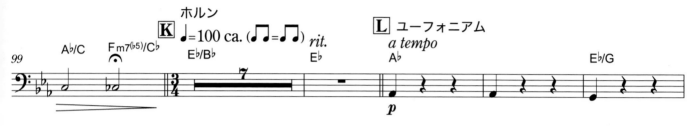
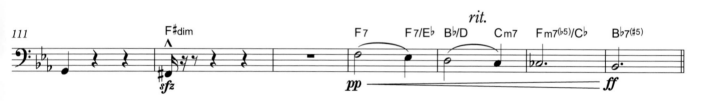
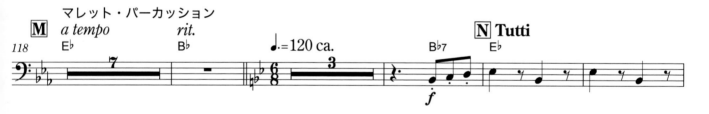

String Bass

楽器紹介のための
ミッキーマウス・マーチ
Mickey Mouse March ~Introduction of wind instruments~

Jimmie Dodd 作曲
郷間幹男 編曲

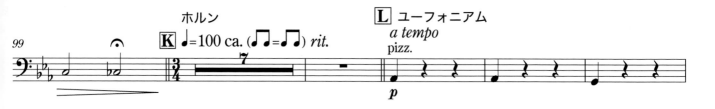
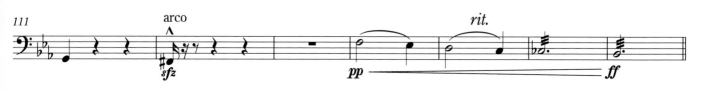
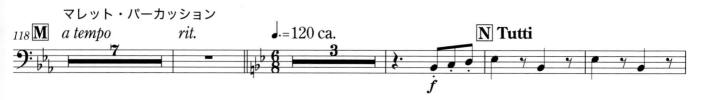

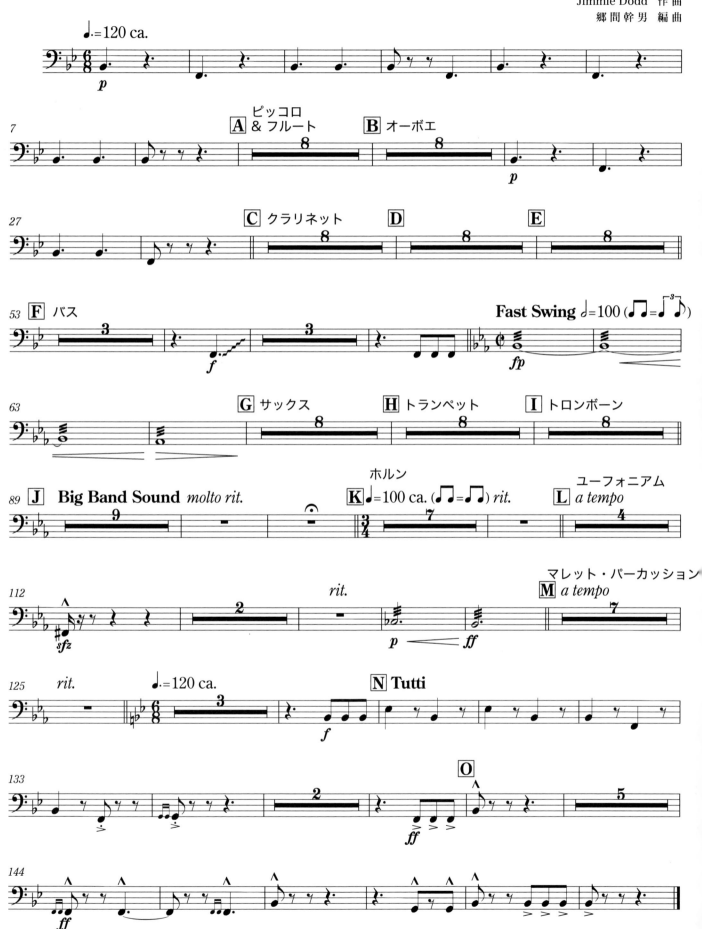

MEMO

Percussion 1
Crash Cymbals, Tambourine, Vibraphone

楽器紹介のための
ミッキーマウス・マーチ
Mickey Mouse March ~Introduction of wind instruments~

Jimmie Dodd 作曲
郷間幹男 編曲

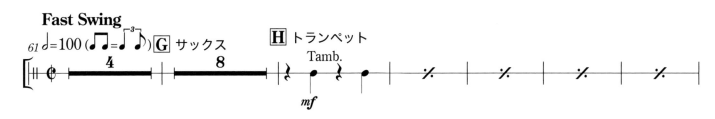

Percussion 2

Bass Drum, Sus.Cymbal, Ratchet, Wind Chime, Sleigh Bell, Flexatone, Glokenspiel

楽器紹介のための
ミッキーマウス・マーチ
Mickey Mouse March ~Introduction of wind instruments~

Jimmie Dodd 作曲
郷間幹男 編曲

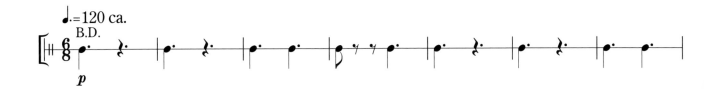
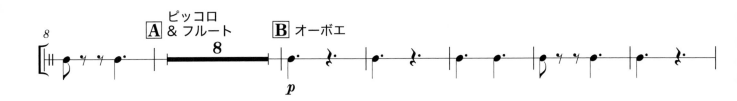

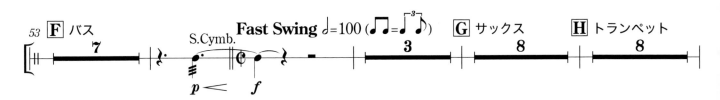

Percussion 2

Bass Drum, Sus.Cymbal, Ratchet, Wind Chime, Sleigh Bell, Flexatone, Glokenspiel

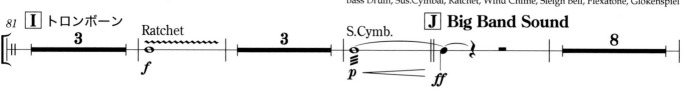
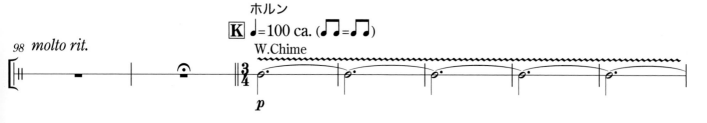
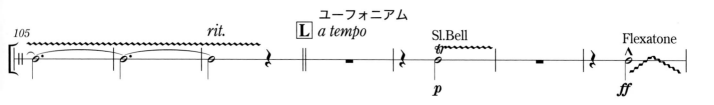
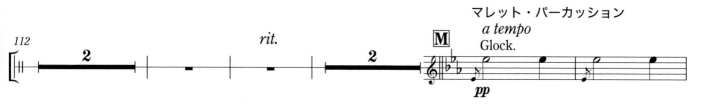

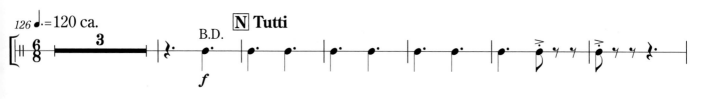

Winds Score
SBL-20-005

Piano Score

楽器紹介のための
ミッキーマウス・マーチ
Mickey Mouse March ~Introduction of wind instruments~

Jimmie Dodd 作曲
郷間幹男 編曲

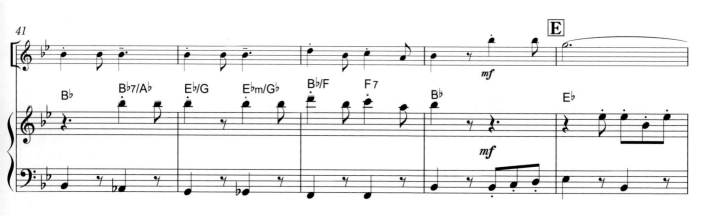

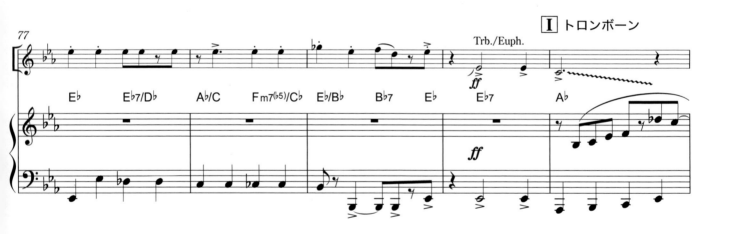
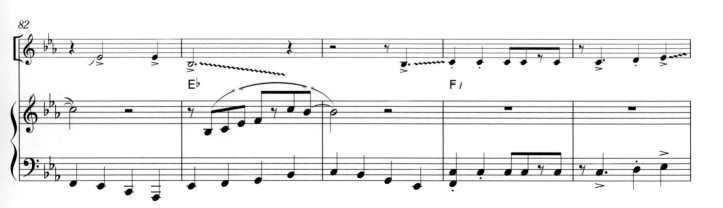

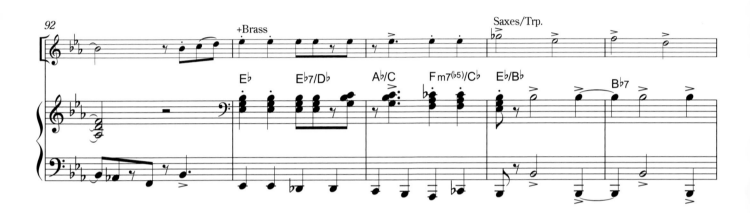
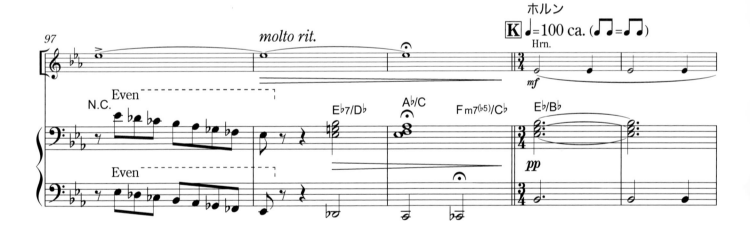

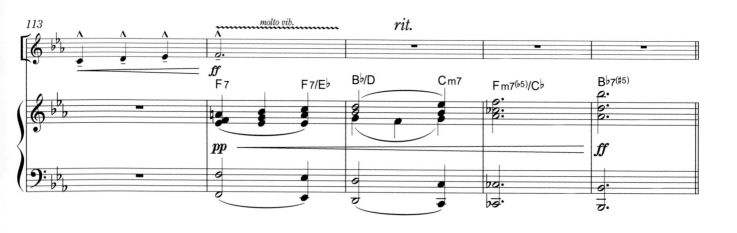

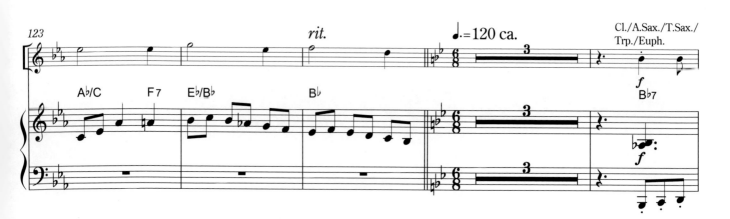

Piano Score

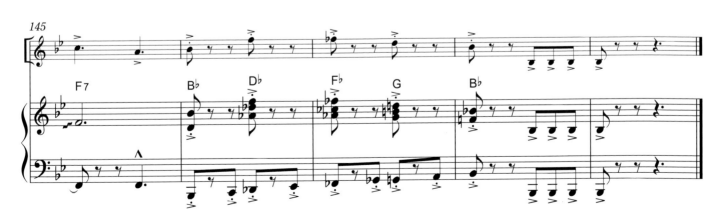